MAKE-UP IS MAGIC

© Patricia Hutchence, 1988

Little Hills Press Pty. Ltd.,
Tavistock House,
34 Bromham Road,
Bedford. MK40 2QD
United Kingdom

Regent House,
37-43 Alexander St.,
Crows Nest NSW 2065
Australia

Designed by Michelle Havenstein
Production by Vantage Graphics
Printed in Singapore by Kyodo-Shing Loong Pte Ltd.,

National Library of Australia
Cataloguing-in-Publication data

Hutchence, Patricia.
    Make-up is magic.

    ISBN 0 949773 82 4
    ISBN 0 949773 87 5 Paperback

    1. Beauty, Personal. 2. Beauty culture.
    I. Smith, Leonie. II. Title.

646.7'26

MAKE-UP IS MAGIC

PATRICIA HUTCHENCE

LITTLE HILLS PRESS

CONTENTS

ACKNOWLEDGEMENTS

Make-up is fun. A wonderful profession, it can be relaxing, artistic, at times frustrating, a challenge, and most rewarding in more ways than one.

. . .A glimpse of a profession I have enjoyed for many years. . .

It has been a wonderful experience putting this book together, and my students, past and present, have enjoyed being part of it. Their enthusiasm and interest was always an inspiration, and I thank them. To my sons, Michael and Rhett, who said I could do it, and my daughter and friend, Tina, a very special Thank You.

My thanks to Julie Kusko and Fay for encouragement, Charles for believing in me enough to take a chance, and to Carollanne O'Brien and CIDESCO for the section on skin traumas.

I am grateful to Marvin Westmore for sharing his knowledge in the art of makeup. The faith and confidence he and his brother, Michael inspired in me has led to the special chapter on paramedical applications.

Patricia Hutchence

INTRODUCTION

To Make-up or cover up? – the perennial question for us all. In Makeup is Magic I share my beauty secrets.

We all need to look after our skin, to be aware of the impact of the sun and take precautions. So I take you through the basics; from applying the base and blush, to contouring, with tips for eyes and lips and suggestions for care of mature skin.

With appropriate care, you can always look striking and attractive. We need to acknowledge what our best features are and develop those.

On this magical tour of faces, you can create for yourself a myriad of characters for any party with simple easy steps.

How often have we struggled to create the right face to go with a fancy dress outfit we spent all last night making for one of the children? Advice on various faces for the children and how to create them is contained here. For teenagers and anyone who wants, broken noses and stitches can be created in no time, with sympathy all round when out partying.

In addition to all the wonderful applications of Make-up – themes, looks of various decades – a very important aspect is its application in the paramedical field for corrective treatment.

Birthmarks, bruising, post-operative scars, tattoos, vitiligo can all be hidden effectively with the right make-up application. Blending is the catchword. It is personally very satisfying when someone realises they can hide their 'scar' whatever it is, and very soon they lose their inhibitions and gain in confidence.

Every time you are off to a fancy dress party, or just dressing for work or a social function you can cover your scar yourself, because you are the expert in developing the best characteristics of your face.

Like everything practice makes perfect so please be patient, follow the steps I have given and work at it. In no time, you will have developed your own techniques and be able to show us all that Make-up is Magic.

GETTING DOWN TO BASICS

BASIC EQUIPMENT

I regard the items listed below as the essentials in one's make-up kit.

Bases — assorted, for dry, normal or oily skin.
Blush — powder or creme.
Eyeliners — pencil, powder or creme.
Eyeshadows — wet/dry powder or creme.
Highlight — liquid, creme or powder.
Lipstick — Lipgloss.
Pencils — various, for eyes, lips, shading.
Powder puffs.
Powder — transluscent or talc.
Red-Out or Vanish — for ruddy complexions, broken capillaries.
Sponges — sea sponges or white latex.
Mascara[1] — cake or wand.

1 For hygienic reasons I prefer cake mascara. Though the wand is easier to use it is a definite no-no in my academy, unless it is the property of the user.

BRUSHES

Eyes

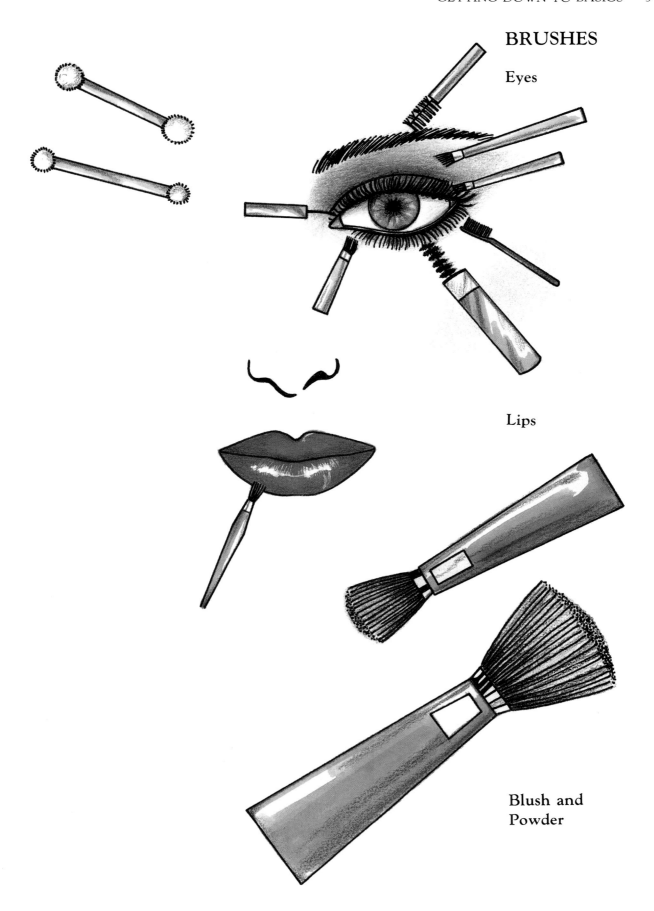

Lips

Blush and Powder

2 A spatula for mixing colours can be bought in an art shop. Smaller spatulas for removing make-up or lipstick from containers are available at cosmetic counters.

A bathroom or kitchen tile is suitable for mixing and blending colours.

Spatula[2] and tile—for mixing colours.
Corrective base (Yello) and Concealer—Yello for brown patches or under eye area on olive skin, Concealer for under eye area on fair skin.

Additional

Face washer; cleanser; moisturiser; toner; eye make-up remover; tissues; cotton buds; cotton balls; tweezers; soap; hand mirror; pencil sharpener; disinfectant; eye drops; nail polish and remover; scissors; hand towel; nail file; lashes.

Hair Aids

Brush; comb; hairbands; clips; spray; gel; shampoo; mousse; ribbons; hair combs.

GENERAL TIPS FOR MAKE-UP ARTISTS

Cleaning the equipment used for making up others

1. Wash gently with warm sudsy water.
2. Rinse with clear cool water.
3. Disinfect, using cool water with a few drops of disinfectant added.
4. Rinse with clear cool water.
5. For stubborn stains use soap or soak in Napisan®.
6. Place brushes, sponges, powder puffs on a towel to dry, preferably near an open window.

I find it is essential that I tidy my work area between jobs (faces). I always ensure that I have a plentiful supply of sponges and brushes. Really, only clean brushes give a true colour, and I never allow sponges to look like Pet Rocks.

At the end of the week, usually at a fixed time, I give the entire make-up kit a thorough cleansing.

Disinfectant is a must. All equipment should be rinsed in water with disinfectant added then in clear water.

Work Area

Here are a few ideas with regard to your work area.

• A well lit work area is important for personal use—or for the professional make-up artist.

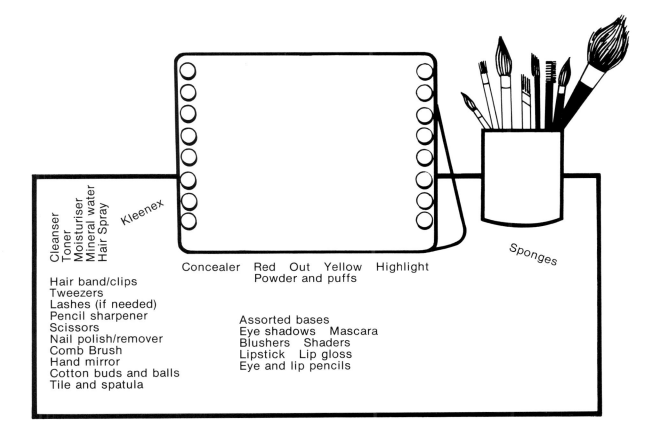

Cleanser
Toner
Moisturiser
Mineral water
Hair Spray

Kleenex

Concealer   Red   Out   Yellow   Highlight
Powder and puffs

Hair band/clips
Tweezers
Lashes (if needed)
Pencil sharpener
Scissors
Nail polish/remover
Comb Brush
Hand mirror
Cotton buds and balls
Tile and spatula

Assorted bases
Eye shadows   Mascara
Blushers   Shaders
Lipstick   Lip gloss
Eye and lip pencils

Sponges

- Portable mirrors are available, and come with lighting around outer frame. They are double sided with one side magnified and the professional make-up artist should have one to carry at all times on location work.

- The chair should be comfortable, and preferably adjustable to the correct height, as the make-up artist should be at eye level with the subject.

- Brushes and sponges should be plentiful and clean.

- Equipment should be replaced after use in order to save searching for that elusive brush, etc.

General guidelines for professional conduct that I have followed and believe essential.

- As in all things it is most important to pay attention to detail.

- Act in a professional manner at all times, because often you can be faced with a real 'dragon', and you just have to remember you have a job to do.

- Be prepared for all jobs—no matter how big or small, they require the same attention.

- Be critical of your own work.

- Remember—less is best—it's easier to add than remove.

- Unless a certain look is specified, design your own.

- Collect a picture file for reference. Visit libraries.

- Study face shapes and prominent features.

- Always be punctual.

- Dress neatly and correctly. (Don't wear high heels on a beach location.)

- Always have a clean well stocked kit.

- Allow 15 minutes preparation time to set out equipment.

- Leave your work area clean and tidy.

SKIN—TO MAKE-UP OR COVER UP?

Ask any little girl which is her favourite or most beautiful doll—the Cabbage Patch Kid, or the Barbie Doll. Invariably the answer is 'I love them both, they are both beautiful'.

However, as these little girls begin to mature, they begin to emulate their favourite rock star, movie star, or whoever is 'in' at the time. The 80s has seen a surplus of Madonnawannabe's, Marilyn's, etc., but we don't see too many Cabbage Patch identikids out there.

No matter what they inevitably decide upon, while it is fun experimenting, finding fun ways with hair/make-up, clothes, it is never too early to learn a proper skin care routine. It is as important as learning to use make-up correctly.

Whether you use soap and water or a cleansing cream is irrelevant, the most important part of your cleansing routine is to eliminate the soap/cream residue by rinsing well in clear warm water.

I personally prefer the soap/water routine, as it suits my skin, a final rinse or generous spray of mineral water, then apply moisture oil or lotion while the skin is still damp. There are a few non-perfumed, non-alkaline, soaps available in liquid or bar form.

If you have any skin problems, it is adviseable to consult a trained beauty therapist (such as AABTh CIDESCO) who will advise you on the best care for your particular skin problem.

Don't just cover the problem with make-up, it will still be there when make-up is removed.

Never apply make-up over an open wound or any skin trauma. There are excellent products which seal while they heal. Ask your chemist or beauty therapist about these.

Drink lots of water, get enough sleep and keep your hair clean.

If your skin is sensitive, always do a patch test before trying anything new.

SKIN TRAUMAS

There is no reason for anyone to suffer the trauma of skin problems. Seek help through the advice of experts if your skin is troubling you, as there are constant advancements in treatments.

The first step is to have the problem diagnosed. Problems such as eczema, dermatitis, psoriasis, acne, scarring, pimples, capillaries, blackheads, stretchmarks, as well as cellulite, sagging skin, etc. can be successfully treated.

One very successful treatment is the Suntronic and Electroderma System. The system is a natural skin healing process with a 98% success rate when the treatment programme is followed.

Don't put off seeking help from your doctor or beauty therapist. You only have one skin to see you through the rest of your life. Don't take it for granted, give it the best possible care and consideration.

MAKE-UP BASE

SELECTING THE BASE

Four basic skin tones.

PINK. . .FAIR. . .OLIVE. . .TAN

Four basic foundations or bases.

LIQUID. . .CREME. . .STICK. . .PANCAKE

Four basic skin types.

NORMAL. . .DRY. . .OILY. . .COMBINATION

COMPATIBILITY

Choose a colour that matches your skin tone and a foundation that is compatible with your skin type.

Liquid base is the lightest base, and should only be used on clear, normal skin. This is best applied with a damp sea sponge, squeezed in a tissue to remove surplus water.

Creme base can be used on dry, normal or combination skin and is best applied with a dry white latex sponge.

Panstick or Cremestick gives good coverage to any skin. Depending on requirement and application it can be heavy or light. Use a damp sea sponge and blend well all over. The formula for this base was once quite heavy, and was always used for film and photographic work. However the formula now appears lighter, and panstick or cremestick is becoming popular for daily use again.

PREPARATION FOR BASE APPLICATION

Any product I have mentioned in this book has worked for me as a make-up artist, and in my Academy, over many years on various skin types. However, I do recommend that you do a patch test with any new product, especially if you have sensitive skin.

Very few complexions are totally flawless. The three most common problems encountered are:
• Blemishes—open skin lesions.
• Broken capillaries, or red patchy areas.
• Under eye discolouration.

These problems can be disguised with products on the market especially formulated to assist.

Any blemish should be sealed before applying the base with a good cover-up product such as Eskamel® or Clearasil®. Choose a colour closest to your skin tone and apply a small amount on the affected area only, using a cotton bud not fingers.

Broken capillaries or any discolouration can be covered with the use of a primer to neutralise the skin tone. These primers are commonly known as Red-Out, Vanish, Yellow or Mellow Yellow. Red-Out and Vanish have a green tint and are best used on fair complexions, while the Yellow primers are best on tan or dark complexions.

Primers are applied to the problem area with a small piece of white sponge in a press/roll motion.

Under eye discolouration can be helped with the aid of a concealer one or two shades lighter than the base for fair complexions, or the Yellow primer for tan or dark complexions.

If the under eye discolouration has a bluish tint mix a touch of peach colour to the concealer. (This blue tint is usually more noticeable on very fair skin.) The concealer is applied with a small brush, and only to the discoloured area, as the lighter colour could project the illusion of puffy eyes.

BASE APPLICATION

After any necessary preparation has been completed you are now ready to apply the base.

Using a sponge (damp sea sponge or white latex) stroke the base all over the skin area using a soft gentle movement.

Blend the base up to, but not in, the hairline. Turning the sponge, use an area which does not contain any base. Blend well.

If there is noticeable hair growth on the face, stroke the base on in the direction of growth.

If there are any large pores in the skin, use a circular or back and forth motion with the sponge.

Work the base all over to just under the jawline.

With a very young or mature skin remember less is best. A young clear skin should glow, and a heavy application is ageing, especially on a mature skin.

Blend the base well as the more blending the clearer the skin will look. Leave no demarcation line. The secret of a good base is being able to see the skin through it and not the base sitting on top of the skin.

Remember, if you have sensitive skin, to do a skin test before applying any new product to the skin.

BLUSH

Blush (and eyeshadows) are meant to look exactly as they sound 'soft' and colour co-ordinated, unless you are working on a special project.

Regardless of whether your colours are soft pinks, vibrant red/purples, or earthy, the safest application of blush is the softest application. A creme blush should be applied with a white sponge before powdering. A powder blush should be applied with a soft brush after powdering. Apply the powder blush to the back of your hand first, to get rid of excess powder before applying it to your face.

Take a really honest look at your face and then feel your bone structure. For correct placement blush should not be an obvious stripe. Practise applying blush using a different 'shape' both sides of the face. Pull your hair back off your face to study the areas of placement. Keep the application soft as more blush can be added if needed.

If you feel hopeless, just think of the fun you will have trying, besides there are plenty of experts out there to help and advise you. Once you've mastered the art of applying blush, you can start on the eyes.

CONTOURING . . . HIGHLIGHTING. . . SHADING

The Subtle Approach

Contouring to change the shape of features can be achieved, but it requires a light gentle touch. Use a highlight colour one or two shades lighter than your skin tone to bring out the areas requiring prominence, or to accentuate a wonderful bone structure if one is lucky enough to be the proud owner of such perfection. A colour one or two shades darker than skin tone will allow other areas to recede.

It is important to study your bone structure with your hair pulled back off the face. Decide which area or feature you would like to alter, keeping in mind that light projects, dark recedes.

It is important to learn the subtle art of blending before attempting any change to your features. Keep in mind that you are trying to create an illusion. Use a light touch and make sure there is no line of demarcation.

Contouring can be achieved with the use of a darker base, pencil or blush colours. If using a blush or powder for shading, begin with the lightest colour and build up to the look required.

The powder shaders or blush should be used after powdering. Apply blush brush to the back of your hand first to remove any surplus colour.

The use of pencils for contouring requires practice. Don't press the sharp point to the skin, it will leave a hard line which is difficult to blend. Hold the pencil on an angle.

You will need to practice as it is the only way to master the art of this illusion.

Contouring

Covering one side of the face, study each side separately to define the difference in look and shape through the use of shading alone.

Study the shading placement to define the subtle difference in 'bone structure' to either side of the face.

EYE TIPS

- Stop eye make-up immediately any stinging or watering occurs.

- Use disposable applicators or cotton buds if there is any sign of eye infection, and discard immediately.

- Wipe eyes gently before any make-up application, to eliminate any crease lines formed by a build-up of the base, otherwise powder eyeshadow will 'set' creases, then apply a soft beige shadow over the lid area before any colour application. This allows the true colour to stand out.

- Keep plenty of brushes on hand—use one for each colour.

- Make sure you apply mascara to bottom lashes first. This helps eliminate the possibility of messy black spots ruining your carefully blended make-up.

Eye Tips for Contact Lens Wearers

- Insert your contact lens before commencing make-up application.

- If you are using a cotton bud close to the eye area, dampen bud, roll it between the fingers to remove any surplus water and also bind any loose fibres which would cause eye irritation.

- Extreme care must be taken with wearers of contact lens. Use a gentle touch around the eye area.

- Avoid eye shadows containing glitter and I suggest you use a cake mascara, as it doesn't contain fibres for lash build-up.

- Wet/Dry shadows will eliminate powder flecks, which can cause irritation but always remember to remove lens before using make-up remover.

- Use damp cotton wool when cleaning your face. It binds loose fibres and avoids irritation through clinging to lashes.

- Eliminate stray brows at least 30 minutes before make-up to avoid redness.

- Do not use prescription drops other than your own, and discard on due date.

- Don't throw away old mascara wands. Clean and disinfect them as they can be used for eyebrows, or to separate lashes after mascara application.

EYEBROWS

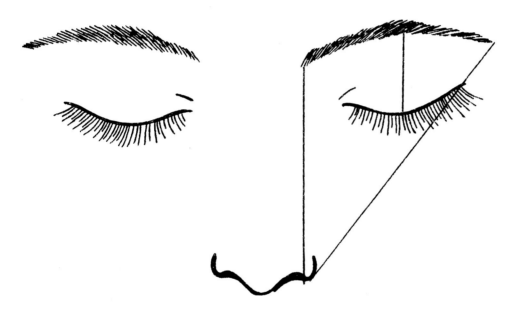

Always remove brows from underneath brow area, not from the top. The chart will help you to determine width and height placement.

Droopy

Remove a few brows from the outer edge, and pencil in from highest point.

Too Low

Remove strays and keep brows brushed up. Highlight the brow area with a touch of eyeshadow underneath. If your eyes are small, keep the colours light.

Thin

Using a very sharp pencil fill in with tiny hair-like strokes.

Thick

If your eyes are small, remove the lower area of brows. If your eyes are large, only remove untidy strays but awlays keep brows well shaped.

If your brows are well shaped but light in colour use a brush-on brow colour, or have a beauty therapist tint them.

EYES

Normal

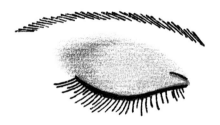
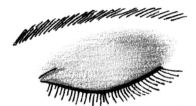

Too Wide

Keep darker colour to inner area.

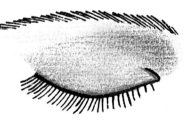
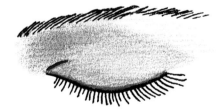

Too Close

Keep darker colour to outer area.

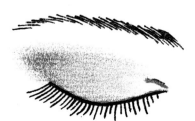

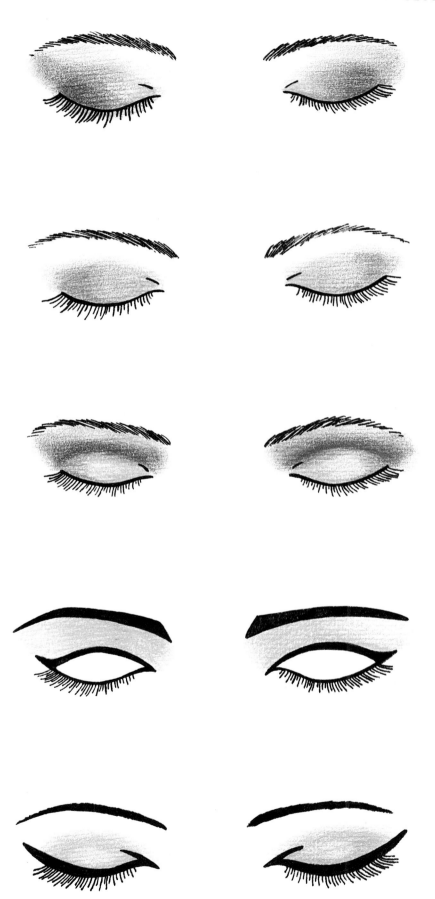

These eyes are the same shape and size. The subtle change in the placement of shadow colours or adjustment to the brows gives a totally different look.

COLOURS

Cool **Hot** **Earthy**

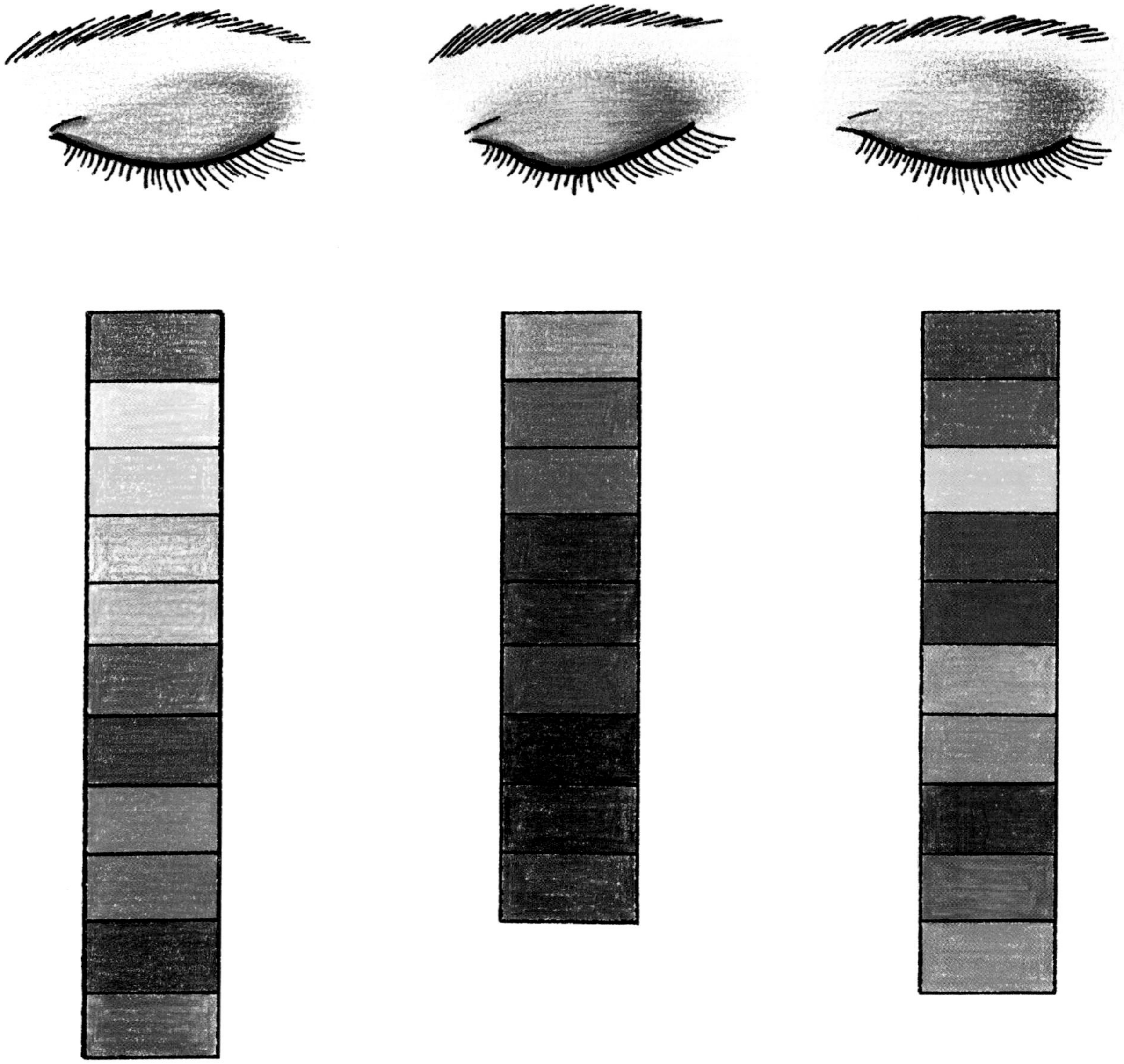

GLASSES

Avoid frosted eyeshadows. The best shadow colours to use are Peach, Pink, Light/Dark Grey, Soft Neutrals, Earthy Tones.

Pay attention to shadows (if any) under eye area.

Keep hair off the face. Take special care with lips.

While we all agree that colour is fun, don't overdo it!
Choose glasses that have frames to cover the eyebrows.

Over the years the words 'you are going to need glasses' were not words one wanted to hear. This is not so today. Glasses are definitely 'in', and come in a variety of shapes, sizes, colours and designs.

Whether you are wearing glasses for purely cosmetic reasons, or as a necessity, there is an incredible range from which to choose. So much so, it can be confusing. Remember, glasses are an expensive item, so take care to choose the right shape and size to suit your face. Generally speaking, the shape of your face tends to dictate the right shape for your glasses, e.g. round face—round glasses; fine features—smaller frames; heavy jawline—rectangular, heavy frames.

- If you can only afford one pair be sure the design or colour is not too fussy, as it could limit your wardrobe.

- Be sure your eyebrows are not visible on top of the frames. This tends to give a perpetually surprised expression to the face.

- Do wear make-up, but avoid heavy colours with sparkle, especially if you are in the mature age group.

- Flat eyeshadows in Peach, Pinks, Soft Grey and earthy tones tend to open up the eyes.

- Wear eyeliner and/or kohl.

- Eliminate any dark shadows under the eyes or in the socket with a cover stick.

- Always keep eyebrows tidy and well shaped.

- Smoother hairstyles tend to suit glasses with heavier frames.

LIP TIPS

For hygienic reasons scrape lipstick with a spatula, place it on your tile, and work from there. Do not apply lipstick directly from the case unless it is your own.

I think it is better to apply lipstick with a brush, as it gives a softer, smoother finish.

When using a lip pencil to give definition to the lipline, be certain it has a sharp point. Do not press too hard as the lip movement will result in an uneven line.

If there is any sign of a cold sore on lips use a cotton bud for application, and discard it immediately.

For longer staying power use powder pencil, or even blush, before lipstick application.

Don't throw away the 'bits' left in the bottom of the case, scrape them out with your spatula and mix them on your tile.

Buy a small clear plastic container for storing your lipsticks. It saves opening dozens of lipsticks searching for a particular colour, and lightens your load.

Make-up For Mature Skin

If you would like a change and are not too adept with your make-up application, get some advice from a make-up artist.

If you are able to experiment with confidence, try a completely new look — the old one could be ageing. Remember, less is best. A heavy application of base tends to creep into those tiny lines.

If your skin is in good condition, use a liquid base, applied with a damp sea sponge.

If a slightly heavier base is required, use a creme base applied with a white sponge (dry).

I suggest you try using a brush on powder for the eyebrows instead of a pencil.

You have to be careful not to over powder. Dip a powder brush into the powder, shake off excess, then gently brush over your face. If your skin is extremely oily, a tissue or damp chamois gently pressed to the skin before powdering will remove excess oil.

Make sure you place your blush correctly. If it is too close to the nose you may end up with a clownish effect. Use the barest minimum and add to it if necessary, to avoid a 'striped' look.

Frosted eyeshadows are not for you. A flat powder or creme shadow is best.

Use a blush, pencil or powder on the lips before lipstick application for a lasting effect. Apply lipstick with a lip brush.

I find that lipgloss tends to 'bleed', so I suggest you avoid it.

PARTY FACES

This book is meant to be fun as well as helpful.

On the following pages I have 'made-up' one side of the face, leaving the other side to be made up.

Draw the outline with a pencil before applying any colour. This enables any corrections to be done, and gives a clearer picture of different changes to the features.

• Pay attention to detail.

• I have included some empty pages in the back of the book for you, the artist, to design your own make-up/fantasy.

• Remember when doing so that what is suitable to the 'flat' face does not necessarily apply to the real thing. Keep in mind bone structure, the areas which project and those which recede, and work with that in mind.

• Have a practice run before making a final decision on design. If it works keep it for future reference.

• Decide on the theme. Remember that certain designs can distort features.

• When using the design, try to match the face to the design. In other words, typecast. Practise first. If it works, make a note of every detail and keep it for future reference.

PREPARATION FOR APPLICATION OF FANTASY FACE

HOW TO APPLY A WHITE BASE

Most fantasy make-up works best on a white or very pale base, but extreme care must be taken to prepare the skin beforehand, as patchy areas will appear and work will look streaky. Pancake, in dry cake form, and liquid type water bases are best used for fantasy, as they do not smudge easily, and do not need powder.

Pancake is applied with a damp sea sponge. If using black on white, do not apply the black too heavily to begin, as it tends to 'bleed' into the white. If the subject has a problem area, apply a product[1] which will seal while it heals before applying make-up.

1 Products, such as Eskamel® and Clearasil® , are available in skin tones. Ask your chemist or beauty therapist to recommend one.

An underbase in peach or ivory will neutralise a dark skin tone and give an even tone to the white base. If using a creme, powder well to set the base before any further make-up application. Creme base is best applied in a press/roll motion using a dry white latex sponge.

Eyeshadows and blush colours are plentiful, and work well for fantasy make-up.

Design outlines are drawn in first with a soft pencil, using as little pressure as possible. Avoid smudging by resting your hand on a tissue.

A practice session is recommended beforehand to determine skin type, base selection and application. Dry or over oily skin needs special attention to obtain a smooth look with sharp clear lines.

Sensitive skin requires a patch test at least 12 hours beforehand.

HOW TO BLOCK OUT EYEBROWS

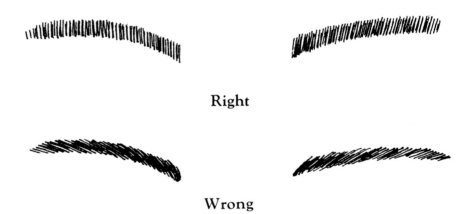

Right

Wrong

- Place a little hair gel on a brow brush. Brush the brows up and flat against the forehead.
- Using a spatula, work in enough wax to hold the eyebrows up and flat.
- Dip a cotton bud in spirit gum or sealer, apply it to the wax in a press/roll manner. Using a clean cotton bud repeat the press/roll movement over the brows. This removes any surplus spirit gum.
- Using a small piece of white sponge, apply powder to brows in a press/roll motion. Allow it to set.
- Apply base. Re-powder. (Creme and panstick bases are best used over brow blockout.)
- To remove the wax from brows, run a piece of cotton thread through the wax. Comb it out with a brow

brush/comb. Any excess wax can be removed using a cotton bud dipped in isapropyl alcohol, keeping eyes closed, or down, to avoid any contact with the eyes.

- Soap may also be used in place of Derma-Wax to block out eyebrows. Place a bar of soap in a bowl of water to soften for at least 2 hours. Leave the top end of the soap out of the water to use as a 'handle'. Apply the soap to the brows in the same manner as the wax.

HOW TO BLOCK OUT HAIRLINE

- Soften bar of soap as described in 'How to Block Out Eyebrows'.
- Part hair across top of head (from ear to ear) about 5 cm from hairline.
- Apply soap liberally along part. Part hair again closer to natural hairline, apply soap along part (similar to method used for tinting hair). Brush hair back after each parting.
- Continue until all hair is brushed back and soap completely covers the front 5 cm of hair.
- Allow to dry thoroughly.
- The same base that is used for the face can now be applied to the new 'high forehead'. It is not necessary to use powder on this section.

CHILDREN'S FACES

BUNNY
Model: Erin

- Apply white base all over the face.
- Powder well with talcum powder.
- Draw eye, nose and mouth outlines, whiskers and teeth with a soft Black pencil.
- Apply Pink eyeshadow.
- Colour the mouth using Pink blush or eyeshadow.
- Apply sparkle to mouth and eyes.
- Re-define lines if necessary.

'Practise' first by drawing in other side with a soft pencil. 'Make-up' as above.

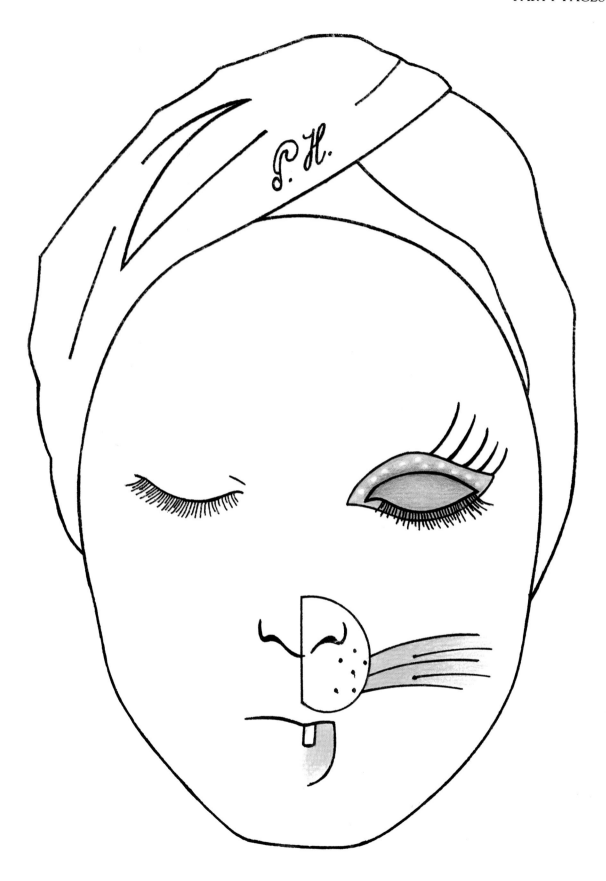

DOLL FACE
Model: Stevey

- Use a very Pale Pink Base over the whole face.
- Powder well with palest transluscent.
- Apply Pink eyeshadow.
- Use a bright Pink blush and Hot Pink lipstick.
- Paint in extended lashes at outside corners of the eyes, using a water base.
- Add sparkle to lips and eye area.

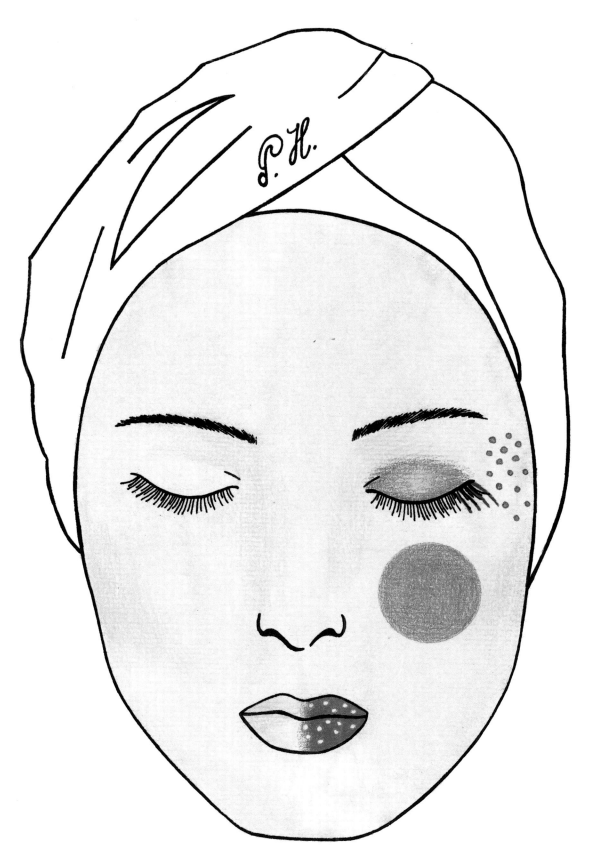

SCARECROW
Model: Jeri

- Use a Yellow base.
- Powder well with transluscent powder.
- Apply Dark Grey eyeshadow to lids.
- Use Peach lipstick.
- Draw in lines and stitches using a soft Black pencil.
- Make a few knots from black cotton thread and attach to the face with eyelash glue.

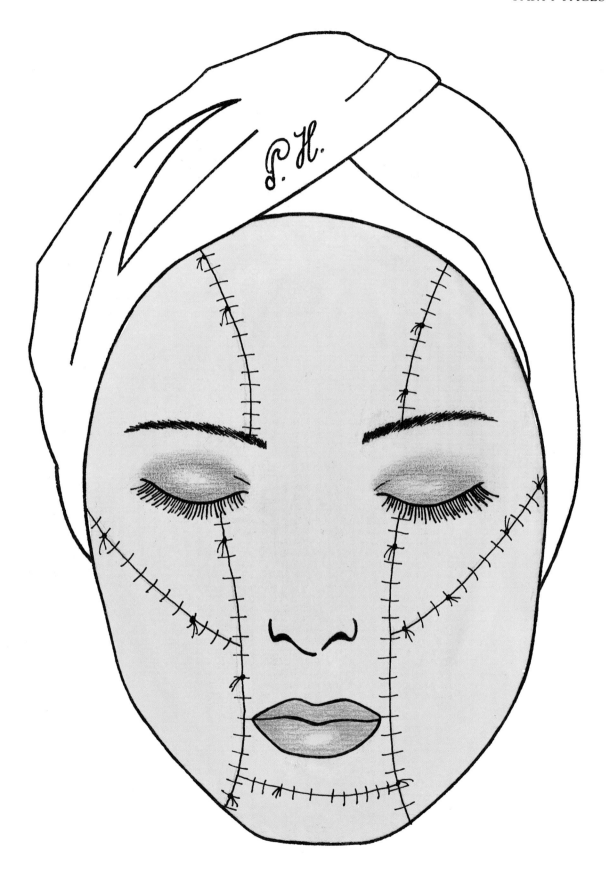

SCARY SKELETON
Model: Andrew

- Apply White base all over face and body.
- Powder well with talcum powder.
- Draw eyes, nose, mouth outlines with a soft Black pencil.
- Fill in this area with Black pancake or water base make-up.
- Draw ribcage outline.
- Fill in with Black pancake.
- Drape a Black cloth over head.

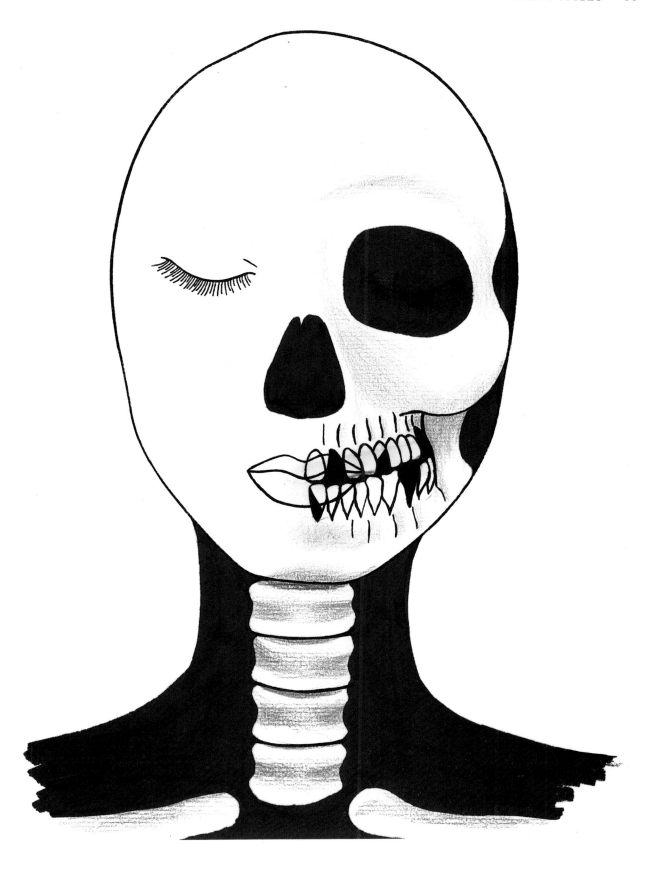

PIGLET

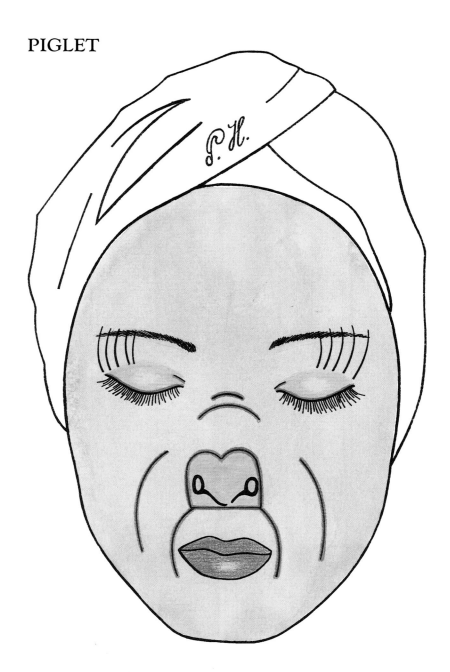

- Apply Pale Pink base.
- Powder well with palest transluscent powder.
- Outline nostrils, and draw and colour in nose and lines on face.
- Use Pink eyeshadow.
- Apply Pink lipstick in full round shape.
- Black Lashes are applied with a pencil, or painted on using a water base.

CLOWN

- Apply a White base.
- Powder well with White Powder, or talc.
- Outline all Black areas using a soft dark pencil.
- Apply Yellow water base or eyeshadow to brow area, eyes and crescent shapes.
- Draw and paint in Red nose.
- Apply Red and Yellow lipstick.
- Use Black kohl all around eyes close to lashes, then add Black mascara.
- Using Black pancake or pencil, redefine Black lines.
- A bow or coloured wig can be added for girl clowns – for boy clowns, a clown wig, or gel with coloured hair spray.

COME AS YOUR FAVOURITE ROCK STAR

Introduction

The idea is to imitate the child's favourite rock star so, Mum, you have to become familiar with the face of the star — colours used, where they are applied, the look created, etc. Then you have to go out and buy the raw material if you don't have the relevant colours in your personal make-up kit, and then apply. Good luck!

WHITNEY WHO
Model: Phoebe

- Apply Dark Olive base.
- Powder well with transluscent powder.
- Darken brows, if necessary. Draw in wing shape.
- Apply Mauve and Purple eyeshadow, extending colour to outer eye area.
- Draw top eyeline and extend the outer edge slightly in an upward slant.
- Apply Black mascara and kohl.
- Use Soft Pink on lips.
- Tease hair or curl. Add a pretty scarf tied in a bow.

LINDY LOPER

Model: Jeri

- Apply Pale base.
- Powder well with transluscent powder.
- Extend brows slanted upwards with Black pencil.
- Use Dark Purple eyeshadows and Black eyeliner in a smudgy fashion.
- Apply Purple to lips.
- Use self-adhesive transfer tattoos.

WILLY IDLE
Model: Nicholas

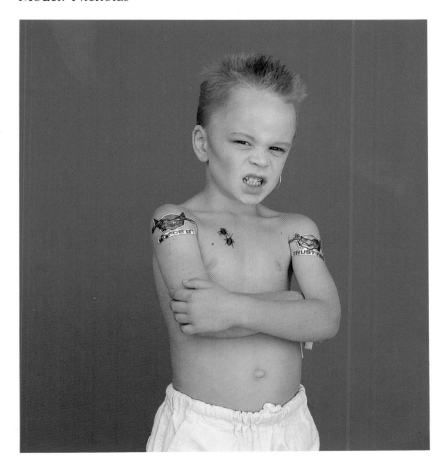

- Apply Pale base.
- Powder well.
- Use Dark Purple blush on cheeks.
- Apply Black to lips.
- Hair is gelled up and sprayed with coloured hair spray.
- Use self-adhesive transfer tattoos.

TEENA 'T'

Model: Erin

- Base used here is Dark Egyptian.
- Powder well with transluscent powder (dark).
- Use Bright Orange eyeshadow, Black kohl all around eye rims and Black eyeliner.
- Apply Coral blush.
- Lips are Bright Orange, with lots of gloss.
- Tease up hair and use dark hair spray if necessary.

FACES FOR ADULTS

PARTY FACE
Model: Sylvia

Draw in a veil, and add sparkles with lash glue, but be careful not to get it on your eyes.

THE MOUSE

Model: Nicole

- Apply a white underbase if you think it is necessary to neutralise the skin.
- Apply White base.
- Powder well with talcum powder.
- Draw outline of the face, the nose, the eyes.
- Fill in outlines with Black pancake or Black eyeshadow.
- Paint in the lips then draw the lines at the outer edge

Draw in the other side of the illustration for practice, if you wish, before applying to your face.

PIERROT

Model: Nicole

- Block out eyebrows.
- Apply Peach underbase.
- Apply White base.
- Powder well with talc, or Pale Pink powder.
- Draw and colour in brows.
- Eyeshadows should be in shades of Pink or Mauve.
- Apply blush in same tone as the eyeshadow.
- Paint the teardrop on the cheek, or attach a coloured stone with spirit gum or eyelash glue.
- Paint in long eyelashes and apply mascara liberally to create a heavy look.
- Outline lips with a pencil and then apply a lipstick.
- Add sparkle to eyelids and the teardrop as the last touch.

I suggest you practise first.

WITCHY WOMAN
Model: Vesna

- Apply the palest Grey base and brush up eyebrows.
- Powder well with talcum powder.
- Use a Black eyebrow pencil to thicken brows.
- Apply Black eyeshadow, as in the sketch.
- Use Black and Red eyeliner.
- Apply Black mascara to lashes.
- Outline lips with Black lipliner.
- Apply Red lipstick and lipgloss.
- Use Red and Black blush on cheeks and side of nose.

SOME BIRDS AND OTHER CREATURES

One of the most popular classes at my Academy is the Bird and Animal Fantasy Class. Everyone loves a fantasy, but from my point of view the lesson plays an important part in learning all about highlighting and shading.

This is illustrated on the following pages. The skin of the Snake, the 'eyes' of the Kestral, the 'tongue' of the Macaw, demonstrate the importance of correct placement of a highlight or shadow to give an illusion, and this is what make-up is all about — an illusion.

MACAW
Model: Nicolette

- Apply White base.
- Powder well if using a creme.
- Draw eyebrows. Outline beak and mouth area with soft pencil.
- Apply Black pancake to mouth and chin area.
- Paint feathers around eyes and chin.
- Apply Green base to forehead and hair.
- Brush in Yellow feathers.
- Paint in Pink tongue.
- Apply White to highlight beak.
- Use Black kohl around eyes.
- Apply Yellow to neck and ears, and Blue to body.
- Brush in Brown feathers.
- Spray hair Blue.

KESTREL
Model – Ailsa

- Apply primer if necessary.
- Use palest Grey base all over face, neck and ears.
- Powder well.
- Draw eye outline with a soft pencil.
- Paint inside outline with Black pancake.
- Outline and paint in beak with Black pancake.
- Highlight eyes and beak with White base.
- Paint Yellow markings around eyes and top of beak.
- Paint in the two dots on beak.
- Brush in Black feather marks on side of beak, neck and ears.
- Brush in White feathers as above.
- Spray hair Black. Paint feathers in Black and White on forehead and hair area.

PEACOCK

Model — Mary-Anne

- Apply White base all over the face.
- Powder well with talcum powder.
- Apply Blue eyeshadow as blush.
- Draw an outline of the eye and nose area (as in photograph).
- Redefine these lines with a fine brush using Black pancake or Black eyeshadow.
- Apply Blue/Green/Purple eyeshadows.
- Use Dark Blue eyeliner around eyes, and Black or Dark Blue kohl around rim of eyes (inside).
- Apply Blue or Black mascara.
- Outline outer edge of lips with Dark Blue pencil.
- Draw a Black line around outer edge of Blue.
- Paint lips White.
- Paint in 'feathers' with Navy, Gold, Green and Purple eyeshadows on forehead, ears and body.
- Gel the hair back and add feathers.

BUTTERFLY
Model — Melinda

- Apply Ivory base all over face and neck.
- Powder well.
- Draw the outline of the butterfly with a soft Red pencil.
- Paint in the outer edge of the wings with White base. Powder with White powder.
- Draw in Black markings on wings, and colour centre area of wings Black.
- Using a small brush apply Red blush to 'body' of the butterfly, then redefine the Red on outer edge of wings.
- Add Silver and Red sparkle to areas on wings and body.
- Apply Red lipstick and sparkle to lips.
- Gel two thin strands of hair for feelers.

THE OWL

Model—Penny

- Apply Orange base all over face.
- Black outline around eyes.
- Draw beak outline with a soft Orange pencil.
- Paint in Yellow beak.
- Paint Black dots on beak.
- Use Yellow on eyelashes.
- Brush stroke feathers in Gold, Yellow, Black, White and Dark Orange.

You can make the hairpiece out of a feather duster pulled apart and arranged around head and neck.

GANG-GANG COCKATOO

Model – Simone

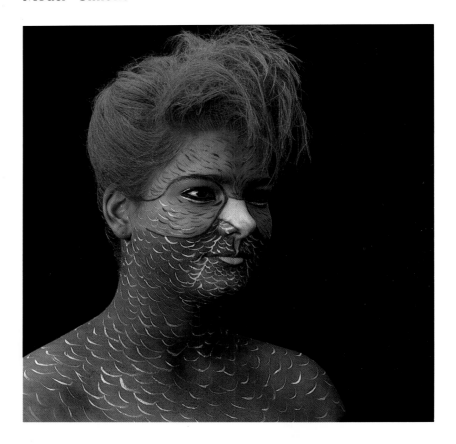

- Apply Orange base to upper part of face and ears.
- Outline eye and 'beak' area using a soft Brown or Grey pencil.
- Apply Grey base to lower part of face and neck.
- Brush on White feathers. Follow pattern around the mouth area.
- Brush on Brown feathers.
- Apply Ivory and Yellow to beak and bottom lip.
- Use Black kohl around eyes.
- Outline eyes with White.
- Tease hair to crest and spray with Orange hairspray.

TURACOS (AFRICAN)

Model – Amanda

- Block out eyebrows.
- Apply Olive base all over face and shoulders.
- Powder over face with Gold.
- Apply Green eyeshadow to lids.
- Apply Gold/Bronze glitter eyeshadow to nose and lips.
- Paint White and Black markings around the eye area.
- Paint Green/Gold/White feathers on face, body and ears.
- Spray the hair Green.
- Add cotton wool for 'snow' effect.

LIONESS
Model – Helen

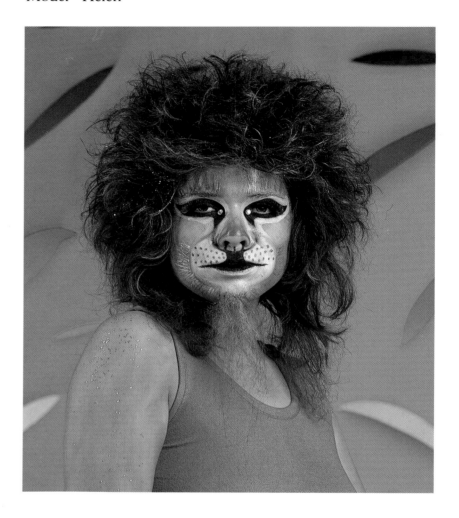

- Apply Golden Brown base all over face, shoulders, arms, hands.
- Powder well with transluscent powder.
- Apply Bronze shading to cheeks, forehead and nose.
- Outline eye, nose and mouth area using a soft Grey pencil.
- Fill in Black areas using a flat Black eye shadow or pancake.
- Apply White base and powder well.
- Using a small brush add Gold whiskers.
- Apply Black dots with a pencil.
- Apply diamantes to eye area with spirit gum or eyelash glue.
- Add whiskers of crepe hair with spirit gum.
- Tease hair to a 'wild' look and apply some glitter gel.

ZEBRA
Model — Melanie

- Block our eyebrows.
- Use primer if needed to cover under eye area discolouration.
- Apply White base, pancake or panstick.
- Powder well with White powder or talc.
- Zebra stripes are Black pancake (water based).
- Use Black kohl around eye rims.
- Colour lips with Black lipstick.
- Hair is gelled and teased on top.
- Cut out stencils to match face markings.
- Place on hair and spray with Black hairspray.

SNAKE
Model – Isla

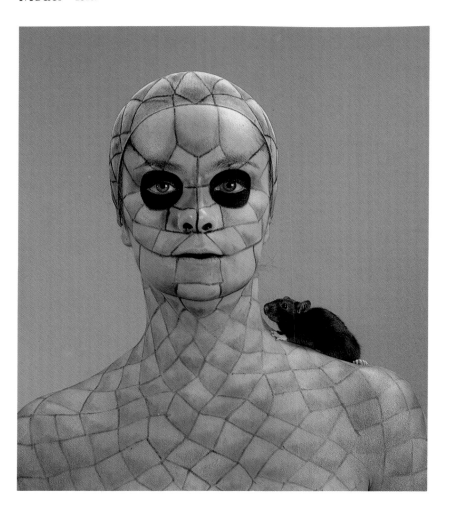

- Apply base all over face and body. Colour used here was a mixture of Ivory and Yellow.
- Pencil in skin outline with a soft Brown pencil, following pattern.
- Outline eye shape and fill in with Black eyeshadow.
- Using a soft brush, highlight and shade the 'skin' with Brown, Gold and Deep Orange eyeshadow.
- Apply Black lipstick in thin lip shape, and around nostril area.
- Head is covered by a stocking, painted to match face markings and colours.

A FEW MAKE-UP TRICKS

On the following pages I have added a few party make-up ideas. They are fun to do, and most of the basic equipment needed can be bought from a chemist, beauty supply shop, theatrical supplier, novelty shop or costume hire outlet.

Basic equipment

Artificial Blood — comes in bottle or gelatine capsule form.

Burn Kit — contains the four basic colours to simulate burns. Red, Black, Orange, Carmine.

Bruise Kit — contains the four basic colours to simulate bruises. Yellow, Lavender, Carmine, Black.

Derma-Wax® or False Flesh® — used to build up nose, chin areas, moulding bumps, cuts, etc.

Eyelash Adhesive — used to apply false eyelashes. Can also be used when small amount of latex is needed.

Gel — Hair Gel — used to slick hair back, helps to keep eyebrows in shape.

Glycerine — used to give all over body shine, or perspiration.

Latex — for ageing, moulding prosthetic pieces such as eyelids, eye bags, etc. Also white latex sponges.

Liner Colours — come in stick form — various colours available. They are easy to apply.

Nose Putty — for building up nose, chin — though harder to mould than wax.

Poring Sponge — Black — containing little holes or 'pores'. Used to simulate skin pores on wax, scratches, stippling colours on beards, etc.

Spatula — small spatulas for removing make-up from jars — available at beauty supply shops. Large spatulas generally are available in art shops.

Spirit Gum — used to help wax or nose putty 'grip' skin. Also useful for attaching beards, moustaches.

Spray Bandage — works as a 'sealer' over wax cuts, etc. Must not be used near eyes.

Again do not use any product unless a patch test is done beforehand.

BROKEN NOSE OR BUMP

- Using a cotton bud, apply a touch of Spirit Gum to the bridge of the nose, just slightly off centre. Be careful not to use it too close to the eyes, nor on an open wound.

Broken Nose—Stitched Wax Cut

- When it feels 'tacky' place a small piece of Derma-Wax®, False Flesh® or nose putty on the spirit gum. Then rub a small amount of gel into the fingers, blend the outside area of wax to the nose (the gel stops the wax from feeling sticky).
- Using a spatula or fingers, mould the wax into a bumpy off-beat shape, being careful to blend the edges avoiding a demarcation line between wax and skin.
- Powder well, using a cotton ball. Leave a few minutes to set. Brush surplus off with a soft powder brush.
- Press 'break' gently with a black poring sponge to eliminate the smooth look of wax.
- Apply a base colour to match skin tone.
- Using a bruise kit or similar colours, apply colour to simulate swelling to eye and nose area, and accentuate the 'break'.
- If using a spatula, keep it free of wax to avoid it lifting. Use extreme care around eye area, especially if fingernails are long.
- To remove wax, run a piece of cotton thread down nose, away from eye area. This will lift the wax from the skin.

WAX CUTS

- Place a small amount of spirit gum to the 'cut' area. Wait until it feels tacky. Apply a small piece of Derma-Wax® or False Flesh® to area. Using a spatula, work wax to desired length and width.
- Blend the edges with a spatula, to eliminate demarcation between wax and skin.
- Using the tip of the spatula, gently cut through the centre to the required length. Seal the cut with a spray bandage, but be extremely careful not to spray near the eyes. It is important to shield the eye on that side.
- Powder well using a cotton ball, then gently brush off surplus powder, and apply a base if you think it is necessary.
- Paint inside the cut area with a Red creme stick, or Carmine colour from bruise kit and apply artificial blood with an eye dropper.
- Be careful—too wide a build-up with wax will look unnatural.

Bruising

BRUISING

- Using a bruise kit, or the colours Yellow, Lavender, Carmine and Black, stipple highlight colour (Yellow) on bruise area to simulate swelling.
- Stipple Lavender around the edges, overlapping the Yellow.
- Stipple Carmine colour over the Lavender and in other areas of 'swelling', keeping in mind that bruises are patchy and discoloured, not even, so they do not have to be perfectly blended.
- A touch of Black may be added to the above colours, depending on the amount of bruising required.
- Powder 'bruise'. Press a damp chamois to area to 'set' it.

Bruise kit contains four colours – Yellow, Lavender, Carmine Red, Black.

LATEX CUTS

- Tear tissue into small strips, removing any straight edges.
- Pour a small amount of latex on a tile, and place a small piece of tissue over latex, then apply more latex over tissue.
- Using a spatula, mould cut into the desired length and width.
- When the latex is dry attach it to the skin with spirit gum and colour in as required.

SCABS—COLD SORES

- Using a cotton bud, apply a few drops of latex to required area. Eyelash adhesive can be used instead of latex. Latex is not to be used too close to eyes.
- Sprinkle a small amount of brown sugar and coffee on to the latex, and add a few more drops of latex over area to seal it.
- Dry with a hand dryer but make sure the dial is on cool.
- Using a very fine brush, paint around the edges of 'sore' area in a Carmine Red colour. (Don't overdo the redness.)

STITCHES

- 'Stitches' are quickly simulated by making a knot in one end of a piece of cotton thread. Cut thread to approx. 3 cm.
- Make the required number of 'stitches'. These can be used on a wax cut, or as in the Scarecrow, and are attached to the skin with latex, eyelash adhesive or spirit gum.

PERSPIRATION

3 parts glycerine
1 part water

- Mix in a plastic spray bottle, use for body perspiration.
- To apply to lip or forehead area, protect eyes with tissue, especially if contact lens are being worn.
- It is best to use a sea or stipple sponge for facial area.

Glycerine can also be applied direct, to give extra shine to the body if required.

DIFFERENT CULTURES, DIFFERENT LOOKS

The looks of those of us in Western Countries have in many ways been shaped by the influence of vastly different cultures. The body painting of the Nuba Tribe, the artistic Mehdi (Henna) painting on the hands and feet of the Indian bride spring to mind, as do the colourful feather and shell headgear of the New Guinea highlanders. Looks of the movie stars and fashion leaders of the 20th century shape what we mere mortals do and wear.

They make a statement, so we witness a seemingly endless procession from Cleopatra to the vamp look of the 20s. The flower child of the 60s, the graphic design of the rock group, Kiss, and the Punk look of the 70s—all had something to say.

On the other hand the 80s have seen the return of the 40s, 50s, 60s for day, and fantasy for evening.

Make-up allows us to be whoever we want to be.

ABORIGINAL INSPIRED

Model: Lorraine

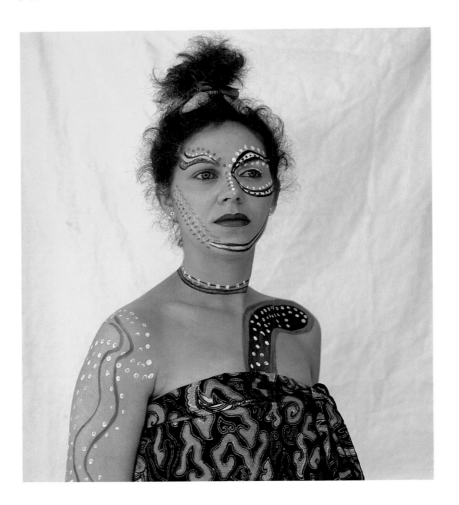

- Apply Dark Olive base all over face and shoulder area.
- Powder well with transluscent powder.
- Using soft Black pencil outline around the eye area, down the side of the cheek and under the chin.
- Paint in the White area, and the Yellow around the eye.
- Whiten the eyelid on one eye only.
- Paint in Rust over the other eye, and add White dots over the Rust, down the side of the nose and across the forehead.
- Apply little Brown dots to areas outlined.
- Use Black mascara.
- Paint the little designs on the other cheek as shown, or what you think appropriate.
- Redefine the dark pencil outline with a brush using a Black pancake.
- Apply Dark Brown lipstick.

EGYPTIAN

- Apply a dark base.
- Draw in Black extended brows.
- Apply Blue, Green and Gold eyeshadows as shown.
- Use Black eyeliner, and kohl around eye rims.
- Apply Black Mascara.
- Use Bronze Blush on cheeks.
- Outline lips with Dark Brown pencil and apply Bronze lipstick and Gold gloss.
- Add sparkles to the corners of the eyes with lash adhesive, or paint in Gold dots.
- False lashes may be needed.

Draw and colour in opposite side.

MAORI—MOKO

- Apply dark base all over face.
- Powder with transluscent powder.
- Draw in design outline with a soft Black pencil.
- Add dots.
- Redefine the darker areas with Black eyeshadow or pancake, using a fine brush.
- Use Orange eyeshadow.
- Apply Black kohl around eyes and Black mascara to lashes.
- Use Dark Brown lipstick.

Draw in opposite side.

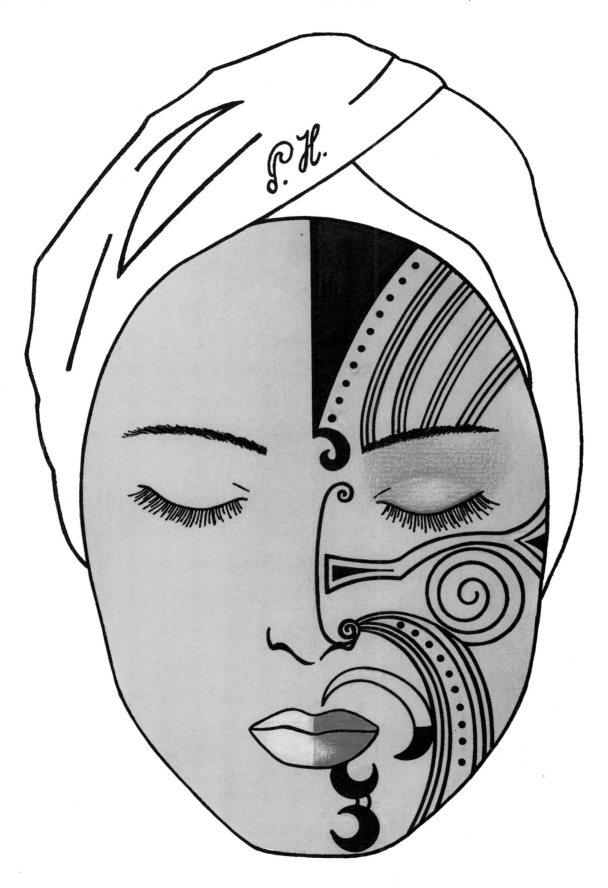

RENAISSANCE
Model: Sylvana

- Block out eyebrows and soap out hairline.
- Apply Ivory underbase, then Ivory/White base.
- Powder well with White powder.
- Apply Peach eyeshadow and blush.
- Use Black or Dark Grey eyeliner all around eyes.
- Lipstick is in soft natural Peach colour.

CHINESE OPERA
Model: Sarah

- Use White underbase, if necessary.
- Apply White base and powder well with White powder.
- Draw in Black brows, as per sketch.
- Apply kohl around inside eye rim, and eyeliner to top eyelid.
- Starting under brow, apply Blush, as per sketch, with colour stronger near eyes and gradually fading.
- No mascara is used.
- Apply clear Red lipstick in a small bow shape.

KABUKI

- Block out eyebrows.
- Apply underbase and White base.
- Powder well with White powder.
- Draw in eyebrows with pencil.
- Apply Black eyeliner around eye as sketched, and Black kohl inside entire rim of eye.
- Line eyes with Red, as in sketch.
- Paint in 'hairline'
- Use Red lipstick in small round shape.

LOOKS OF THE DECADES OF THE TWENTIETH CENTURY

Fads and fashions in make-up as in dress have changed dramatically over the years. There is always something to learn, that is why make-up is interesting and fun, as well as allowing one to be an individual and to experiment with colour. But when a certain era is called for, do pay attention to detail.

The following looks through the 1920s to the 1970s were the most popular looks of that time.

1920
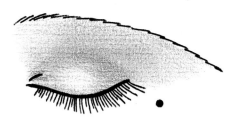

1930
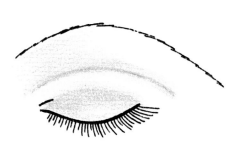

1940

1950

1960

1970

1980

1920

Eyebrows were thin and extended in a downward slant.

Eyeshadow covered the eyelid and blended all the way up to the brow area, through to the end of the brow. Eyeline was drawn along the top and bottom close to the lash line. The 'Vamps' of the day added a Black smudgy line to bottom lash area as well. This was quite thick and usually not blended very well. Mascara was added and lashes were sometimes dotted with wax (on the tips) then more mascara was applied. This gave a thicker look to the lashes.

Lips were drawn in a 'bow' and gloss (vaseline) was added. Some added a beauty spot to the eye or lip area.

- Pale-Natural base.
- Blush (under eye area).
- Mauve or Brown eyeshadows.
- Thin extended brow.
- Smudgy eyeliner under eye.
- False eyelashes.
- Red 'bow' lips.
- Mascara.

Hair

Short—Edwardian style, or finger waved. Worn with a band around forehead.

Long—Plaited or coiled around ears—held in place with combs.

1930

The eyebrows were still thin, but curved and again extended.

Eyeshadow was worn on the lid in the eye socket area close to the nose, with a highlight colour under the brow (in the highest area of the eyebrow). False eyelashes were added and often, although not always, a thin line was drawn in the socket area. Eyeline was drawn on top and bottom, close to lash area. Mascara was used on the bottom lashes, and then through the added lashes to join the false lashes to the natural.

Lips were small, as in the 20s, but rounded in shape.

- Pale base.
- Dusty Pink eyeshadow.
- Blush (under eye area).
- Very fine curved extended brow.
- Raspberry Red 'bee sting' lips.
- Mascara.
- False eyelashes
- Eyeliner, creaseline shadow in eye socket.
- Beauty spot.

Hair
Platinum — short — curls on forehead.

1940

Eyebrows were beginning to thicken, though the extension was not quite as long as in 20s and 30s. There was more thickness closer to the nose area.

Eyeshadow was popular, but mostly worn on the lid not quite up to the socket area. False eyelashes were worn, often half at the outer edge of the eye. Eyeliner was worn fairly thick, close to the lash line, with mascara on top lashes only.

Lips of the 40s were large, almost always over the natural lip line. Study the illustration of lips. You will note that the highest part is at the outer edges (almost a sneer).

- Base dark and heavy.
- Powder.
- Brows, thicker.
- False lashes, long and thick.
- Blush – note position.
- Eyeshadow on lid only.
- Lips, over lip-line, large and glossy.
- Mascara, eyeliner

Hair
'Victory' Roll – upswept. Turbans were worn with a curly fringe.

1950

Eyebrows were more natural in size and shape, though there was a definite arch.

Eyeshadow was pale. Mauve and Blue were popular, and a highlight colour was applied under the brow, a deeper colour at outer edges. Eyeline was drawn along top of lashes extending slightly to an upward flick. The bottom line was extended very slightly. Often these two lines met and were filled in to give a doe-eyed look. Eyelashes were worn, usually at outer edges only. Mascara was applied top and bottom.

Lips were Red, glossy and glamorous. A beauty spot was applied close to edge of top lip.

- Base, pale.
- Powder.
- Brows, winged shape.
- Shadow, Pale Blue.
- Eyeliner, extended to outer edge 'doe-eyed look'.
- Mascara, false lashes.
- Blush—note position in sketch.
- Lips, Red, full.
- Lipgloss.
- Beauty spot.
- Deeper colour in eye socket area.
- Highlight under brow bone.

Hair
Blonde—long, over one eye—short, page boy.

1960

Eyebrows were thick and slightly arched.

Eyeshadow was heavily applied, and the highlight under the brow was in a pale colour to co-ordinate with lid and socket colour. White highlight under the brow was popular. The socket area was a dark colour blending with the lid tone. Eyeliner was heavy, extended out slightly past lash line on top, and applied on bottom lash area. Eyelashes were thick and long, occasionally two pair being worn on top, one pair on the bottom, with extra lashes drawn at bottom lash area.

Lips were the palest Peach, or Pink, or almost White.

- Base normal tone.
- Powder.
- Blush—note position.
- Thick brows
- Highlight under brow in White or pale colour.
- Eyeliner.
- Eyeshadow on lid deeper in socket under brow area (highlight).
- False lashes (top and bottom). Sometimes the bottom lashes were painted in.
- Mascara
- Very pale lips, almost White.

Hair

Teased to a 'beehive', or two or three curly hairpieces were attached to give height to the hair. Also the short geometric Sassoon cut was popular.

1970

The Punk era with colourful eye make-up, upward slanted brows, and Black, Blue or Purple lipstick. It was a time of experimentation.

There were also the 'Flower' people who wore little or no make-up, and painted or tattooed flowers on their faces and shoulders.

- Pale base and powder.
- Brows were sometimes shaved to allow different shapes.
- Eyeshadows and lipsticks were vibrant shades of Orange and Purple, or Black.
- Black eyeliner.
- Black lipliner with coloured lipsticks.

Hair
Straight long hair was popular with men as well as women. Usually worn parted in the centre.

The Punk look started in the 70s. Hair was shaved (men and women) in part, and sprayed with fantasy colours.

1980

Early 1980 saw the remainder of the punk era, and a return to the 50s and 60s. There is no special look for to-day, it is still a matter of trial and error. While having fun with make-up is exciting, wear whatever suits you best—but blend it well.

- Pale base and powder.
- Blush, eyeshadow and lipstick in matte colours. The eyeshadow is in a similar shape to the 1950s.
- Eyeliner is Black or Deep Blue, depending on shadow colour.
- Black kohl is still popular.

Hair
This is the look which has remained popular throughout the 80s. Hair is sleek, whether long or short.
If worn long it is held in place with a bow or comb. If short add a pony tail and/or a braid, and hold in place.

MAKE-UP FOR SPECIAL PROBLEMS

CORRECTIVE MAKE-UP FOR SPECIAL PROBLEMS

After many years spent simulating bullet holes, cuts, bruises, burns, drug addicts, accident victims, etc. I suddenly found myself totally involved in yet another area of make-up. As the result of filming in Hong Kong, I met and worked with Marvin Westmore of Hollywood.

The Westmores are among the leaders in the art of make-up, an art which has been handed down from generation to generation.

This meeting led to an invitation from Marvin and his brother, Michael, to work with them in the relatively new field of Paramedical Make-up. Working closely with Marvin I noted his care, attention to detail, and shared his enthusiasm and gratified feeling when a client (on their doctor's referral) 'saw' themselves for the first time minus scars, birthmarks, etc., and realised that with patience, time, and care they too could master the art of make-up to disguise these problems.

Even the tiniest scar or skin trauma can feel so gigantic to some people. This is understandable as 'books' and advertisements have brainwashed us into thinking we should never be less then perfect. Those with a really big problem have felt that nothing could be done, or that the make-up coverage would have to be extremely thick. In most cases this is not so. Large or small, these problems can lead to trauma or loss of confidence. Hopefully the following pages will be of help.

REMEMBER, LOOKS AREN'T EVERYTHING. . .
BUT A FEW CLEVER TRICKS ARE HANDY!

SPECIAL PROBLEMS

Listed below are a few of the most common skin problems requiring a specially formulated make-up.

Acne scarring.
Birthmarks—light/dark Brown or Wine Red marks.
Bruising—accidental or post surgery.
Chloasma—Brown/Yellow patches.
Chemical peel or Demabrasion.
Scars—accidental, burns or post surgery scars.
Tattoos—names, designs, permanently applied for cosmetic reasons.
Varicose Veins—Blue/Purple, can be flat or raised.
Vitiligo—White unpigmented patches on the skin.

These problems cannot be hidden for any length of time with a normal make-up base, and require an opaque, waterproof make-up which is specially formulated, non-greasy, gives lasting coverage, and prevents these problems from creeping through after a short time.

On the following pages I have made up three models with different problems, and had 'before' and 'after' photographs taken. The problems with these models are acne scarring, facial scars (accidental) and a Port Wine birth mark.

Practise the application techniques, avoiding a mask-like look. Try to match skin tone as closely as possible. If that is difficult then apply one shade darker than the normal skin tone.

Always 'play up' the best features, and in preparing the skin beforehand, cleanse, tone or moisturise it to suit skin type.

PREPARATION FOR APPLICATION OF CORRECTIVE MAKE-UP

It is important to familiarise yourself with the products available today which give a good coverage to any skin trauma. No matter how large or small, or how fair or dark the skin is, there is a colour for everyone.

These products are available in many countries all over the world, so I suggest you begin by making enquiries at your large department stores for these specially formulated products.

A normal product will cover some problems, but not for long, as it must be opaque to give good coverage.

As corrective make-up is a little heavier than normal make-up, I suggest that you also use skin care products to cleanse, and a non-oily moisturiser.

Do not use any product without a skin patch test first, as your skin may be sensitive.

The equipment required before using your product -

Mirror, double sided, one side magnified.
Light, or well lit area facing a window.
Base (corrective) in skin tone, or one shade darker.
Yellow colour (corrective) or yellow tone to remove any dark patchy spots or the red of a birthmark.
Concealer for under eye shadows.
Red Out or Vanish can be used on good fair skin to cover red areas. (Do not use on open skin problems.)
Special setting powder
Small spatulas to remove base from container.
Spatula and tile to mix bases.
Tissues; Brushes; Hair Band; Sponges; Hand Towel; Chamois; Cotton Buds; Powder Puff; Cotton Balls.

It may be necessary to use two bases to get colour required.

TO COVER BIRTHMARK

Before any application of corrective make-up, it is important to consider the age of the person, the size of the birthmark, and condition of the skin.

A young person with a small mark and good clear skin needs corrective only on the birthmark area.

On the next page you see a birthmark before and after application, and though I have applied make-up all over, corrective make-up has been applied only on the birthmark area.

As you can see in the before photograph, Romula has the mark covering her eye, top of her lip, and the side of her face. Romula has a very good skin, and pretty eyes.

I used a Yellow tone first on the birthmark areas only, to reduce the Wine Red colour. This was applied with a white sponge in a press/roll manner, barely overlapping the edges of the mark to eliminate any demarcation line.

I then applied a corrective colour base to match Romula's skin. This was only applied to the birthmark area, over the

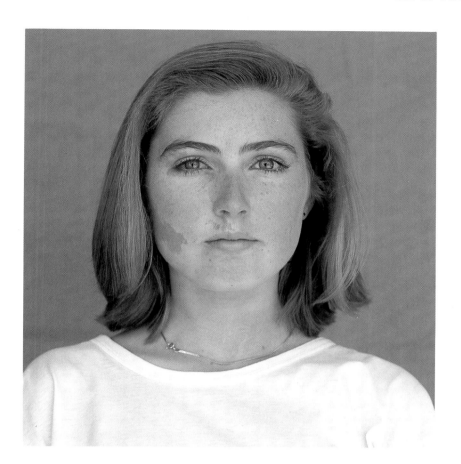

BIRTHMARK
Model: Romula

Before

After

Yellow tone, again using the same press/roll manner. A normal creme base to tone with Romula's skin was applied all over the rest of the face, and lightly covered the corrective area.

Powder (corrective) was applied first to the birthmark to 'set' make-up and stop colour 'creeping' through, then a normal transluscent powder was lightly applied all over, then a touch of blush in a Peach tone. I used a soft Peach and Grey eyeshadows, mascara, and natural lipstick and gloss colour.

TO COVER BRUISING

Bruising, whether it is accidental or the result of surgery, can last for some time. On the facial area it usually is accompanied by swelling, so there are two problems to consider.

If the bruise is heavy, on the leg or body area, it can be covered by the method described in the section on Tattoos.

If on the face, choose a base as close to the skin tone as possible (corrective base). A Yellow base is also required to help neutralise the skin tones.

Corrective powder must be used to 'set', and also to remove shine from the swelling.

The steps are:
- Apply Yellow base colour with a white sponge in a gentle pressing motion.
- Apply corrective base to the bruise area, again in a gentle pressing motion.
- Apply normal base colour all over the face, including the area of swelling.
- Add special setting powder (allow to 'set' for about 3 minutes). Apply this powder to the bruise area only.
- Apply normal make-up to eyes and lips, avoiding any Purple/Blue tones, as they pick up and exaggerate bruise colours.

Normal transluscent powder can be brushed over the make-up, using a very soft powder brush.

PIGMENTATION PROBLEMS— LIGHT AND DARK PATCHES

Pigmentation problems can occur at any time, any age. They affect both sexes, and fair and dark skin alike.

If the skin cells produce too much melanin, dark areas appear. If the skin cells stop producing melanin, then light patches will appear.

These problems can be covered, but require patience and care, especially when the problem is over-production of melanin, as it is always easier to darken a light area, than to lighten a dark area.

Anyone suffering these problems should take extra care to block out the sun's rays totally by using an oil and/or perfume-free blockout every two hours, and by wearing a hat. This is something I cannot stress enough, and it also applies to those of you who have undergone a dermabrasion or chemical peel, as the skin cells can be totally destroyed if exposed to the sun.

I cover vitiligo on the following pages (light patchy areas) and the application of corrective make-up for this particular problem. If, on the other hand, the opposite is the case (dark patchy areas) cover as for vitiligo, matching the corrective make-up to the normal skin tone, but use a Yellow tone first.

If the area to be covered is small, such as perfume, pregnancy or sun spots, cover these areas with 'Yello' (or a Yellow tone) plus corrective base to match skin, applying corrective base and powder only on these patchy areas. Apply normal base all over the face, transluscent powder and make-up as usual.

SCARS

Accidental scars can be large and shiny, small white patchy lacerations, or raised and bumpy.

Acne scars are either red or indented, or both.

Burn scars can be raised and shiny, the result of skin grafts.

Post surgery scars which are bumpy and shiny, require particular care with the application of corrective make-up, as there are two problems here, the slick shine which the majority of make-up products would 'slide' off, plus the indentations which throw off highlight and shadows in certain lights. Unfortunately there is nothing we, as make-up artists, can do about the bumpy areas, but we certainly can help with coverage and disguise as best we can, thanks to the thoughtful makers of various products available today.

One excellent product I have found which gives good coverage to skin grafts or heavy scarring is Dermablend Leg Cover®, which can also be applied on the face or any part of the body.

I mention this product, as I personally suffered the heat of many summers by wearing stockings to cover a large slick scar on my leg, until I discovered this particular product which didn't 'slide' off.

ACNE SCARS

The photographs of Millie on the following page shows the extent of scarring as the result of acne. Millie is fortunate as her scars are not as indented as most acne sufferers' are, and her skin is in good condition otherwise. Most acne sufferers almost always have extremely oily skin, and should get into the habit of using a gentle 'scrub', plus a non-oily moisturiser. A beauty therapist will advise those of you who suffer with this problem on the best product suitable for your skin. Fortunately a lot can be done these days to help the problem.

As Millie has quite a lot of red areas, I first had to neutralise the skin, so I used a Yellow colour all over (except the nose).

Using a corrective base colour to suit her skin, I applied it all over lightly, using a white sponge, in a press/roll motion.

As the cheeks were the most affected, I applied another light layer of corrective base over this area, using the press/roll motion.

Powder was applied with a soft powder puff, and left a few minutes to set, then brushed off gently with a soft powder brush.

Soft Coral blush was then applied.

On Millie's eyes I used earthy Bronze colours, eyeliner, and Black mascara, and Soft Bronze lipstick and gloss were applied to her lips.

If there are heavy indentations in the skin, apply the blush in a circular and back and forth motion, to fill in the indentations, otherwise the colour will sit on top of the skin and emphasise the problem.

ACNE SCARS
Model: Millie

Before

After

Millie, a Melanesian, has dark skin, and as with most dark skinned people, the skin has yellow or purple tones, so neutralise it with a yellow base first.

POST SURGERY SCARS

Cathy has several small laceration scars over her eyes, cheeks, chin, and one long scar down the side of her face to her mouth. Cathy has a beautiful bone structure, and was fortunate to have a good cosmetic surgeon who was able to work the scar in just under the cheekbone area.

Cathy has many broken capillaries and assorted tones in her skin, so I had to neutralise the skin with a green tone before any make-up application.

I then brushed the corrective base in her skin tone on the scar under the chin, under the cheekbone, and on the tiny white scars.

I powdered those areas with a corrective powder, and let it set for a few minutes.

The corrective base was then lightly applied all over (including scar area again) using a white sponge in a gentle press/roll manner.

Powder was applied with a touch of eyebrow powder to strengthen the colour.

I used Grey eyeliner, Bronze and Grey eyeshadows with Black mascara, and Grey kohl pencil on the rim of eye. I then chose Bronze lipstick and Soft Bronze blush.

TATTOOS

These can be covered but lots of practice and patience are required, as they tend to creep through even more than the Port Wine birthmark.

The method below has worked well on the various tattoos I have covered.

Equipment required – Regular base colour; Dermablend® or Covermark® Leg Cover; Yellow corrective base; small brush; soft powder brush; setting powder; white latex sponges; powder puff.

- Using a small brush, apply the Yellow corrective base to the tattoo area, press/roll over this to blend, using a small piece of white sponge.
- Powder lightly, allow to set, and then brush off excess.
- Using a white sponge, apply Leg Cover in a press/roll

POST SURGERY SCARS
Model: Cathy

Before

After

motion, keeping within tattoo area to avoid a demarcation line.

- Powder again, allow to set, brush off excess.
- Apply regular base over this in matching skin tone colour, and powder with a transluscent powder, brushing off excess.
- Some bruising can be treated as above, especially on the body area.
- Lighter bruising on the face can be covered as above, but use a base (corrective) colour to match the skin, instead of the leg cover.

Always do a skin patch test before any make-up application, especially if the skin is sensitive.

VARICOSE VEINS
(or Spider Veins)

Equipment required – Corrective Leg Cover; Yellow corrective base; small brush; cleanser; soft powder brush; white sponge; corrective powder; cotton balls; moisturiser.

- Cleanse area of application.
- Moisturise, leave three minutes to allow moisturiser to 'sink' in.
- Using a small brush, apply the Yellow corrective base to the areas where colour is more prominent.
- Using the white sponge, apply leg cover using press/roll movement, blending edges until there is no demarcation line.
- Using a cotton ball, apply setting powder generously, then leave for a few minutes to set.
- With a cotton ball or very soft powder brush, gently brush off surplus powder.

VITILIGO—LOSS OF PIGMENT

The application of corrective make-up with this problem requires practice, patience and care with blending to avoid a mask-like look. Even the clearest skin in the world can be hidden under a mask of make-up and a heavy hand.

If the problem is minor, choose a corrective colour close to your natural skin tone, plus a regular base in the same tone.

- Apply the corrective base to the light areas, using a sponge or brush, depending on the area to be covered.

- Blend the corrective base to the edges to avoid a demarcation line, using the sponge in the press/roll manner, or feathering out the edges with your brush.
- Set this area with corrective setting powder.
- Using a small piece of white sponge, apply the regular base over the problem area and all over the face.
- Powder again with a transluscent powder. Allow to 'set', then brush off excess.
- Proceed with usual make-up, playing up the best features.
- If the white patches are extensive, the corrective base and special setting powder should be used all over the face. With a white sponge, apply base tone corrective make-up all over in the press/roll manner. (Just a light application is needed.)
- Powder very lightly by dipping the powder brush in the powder, shake off the excess, then brush over face.
- Apply another light base of corrective make-up all over the face. Powder again more generously using a powder puff, leave to set, then brush off gently.
- Apply a damp chamois to the face to further set the make-up. This will give a more natural look, and avoid the mask-like appearance.
- Make-up as usual, playing up the best features. Experiment with different eye colours and shapes.

CREDITS

A very special thanks to the Models—big and small—students and friends, who willingly gave their time to me, and my make-up artists, who contributed their time and talent.

Make-up Artists

Vanessa Clarke
Jane Conlan
Cassie Hanlon
Tina Hutchence
Ailsa McGregor
Danielle Morrison
and Yours Truly

Nicolette Moffatt
Carrollanne O'Brien
Katherine Parkinson
Nicky Roxburgh
Tania Travers
Roselynne Wertheim

Photography

John Adams
Mark Roxburgh

Illustrations

Patricia Hutchence and Leonie Smith

Hair

Tina Hutchence
Katherine Parkinson

Makeup and Illustration front and back cover:
Patricia Hutchence.